HARCOURT

Math

Indiana ISTEP+ Test Prep

Grade 3

Harcourt

Orlando   Austin   Chicago   New York   Toronto   London   San Diego

Visit *The Learning Site!*
www.harcourtschool.com

Printed in the United States of America

ISBN 0-15-339014-X

7 8 9 10   073   12 11 10 09 08

CONTENTS

VOCABULARY REVIEW

Number Sense Vocabulary

Write the word or words from the box that best complete the sentence.

even	odd	fraction	whole	bar graph
less than	greater than	ones	twos	seventh

1. When you count by saying 2, 4, 6, 8, you are counting by

   _____.

2. 56 is _____ 32.

3. You can write 36 as 3 tens + 6 _____.

4. $\frac{3}{3}$ is equal to 1 _____.

5. Susan used a tally table to make a _____.

6. A number that has 0, 2, 4, 6, or 8 in the ones place is _____.

7. 85 is ten _____ 95.

8. The numbers 17, 19, 21, and 23 are all _____ numbers.

9. $\frac{1}{4}$ is called a _____.

10. The letter *G* is the _____ letter of the alphabet.

Computation Vocabulary

Match the meaning and the word.

1. the opposite
   of add •   • sum

2. the answer
   in addition •   • doubles

3. to find out
   ABOUT how many •   • subtract

4. the answer
   in subtraction •   • estimate

5. a fact having two •
   addends that are   • difference
   the same

Write the word or words from the box that best complete the sentence.

```
  addends    column addition    count on    fact family    regroup
```

6. When you add 9 and 2, you can _____ 2 to find the sum.

7. A _____ is a set of related facts, such as
   $2 + 3 = 5, 3 + 2 = 5, 5 - 2 = 3, 5 - 3 = 2$.

8. When you trade 10 ones for 1 ten, you _____.

9. In the number sentence $8 + 3 = 11$, the 8 and the 3 are called
   _____.

10. In _____ first you add the ones and then you add
    the tens.

Algebra and Functions Vocabulary

Write the word or words that complete the sentence.

1. 3 + 4 = 7 is a number _____.

   sentence   **question**

2. You can use a _____ to help you count back.

   plane shape   **number line**

3. A part of a pattern that repeats is a _____.

   pattern unit   **fact family**

4. In 2 + 3 = 5 and 3 + 2 = 5, the sums are the same.

   The _____ of the addends is different.

   order   **number**

5. A hundred chart can help you _____.

   skip-count   **weigh**

6. 3, 6, 9, 12, 15 is a number _____.

   doubles   **pattern**

7. You can group three addends in different ways.

   The _____ stays the same.

   difference   **sum**

8. When you count by saying 51, 52, 53, 54, you are counting

   _____.

   backward   **forward**

9. Dave has 9 crayons. Maria has 5 crayons. You can use

   _____ to find out how many they have in all.

   subtraction   **addition**

10. 4 + 6 is _____ 6 + 4.

    less than   **equal to**

Geometry Vocabulary

Match the word and the picture.

1. triangle   •

2. square   •

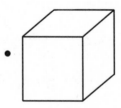

3. rectangle •

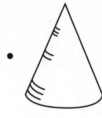

4. cube   •

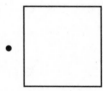

5. cone   •

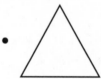

More Geometry Vocabulary

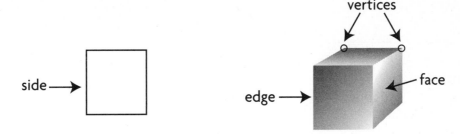

Read the question. Circle the answer.

1. What figure has 3 sides?

   triangle   **square**

2. What figure has 6 square faces?

   hexagon   **cube**

3. What figure has 8 vertices?

   rectangular prism   **pyramid**

4. What do you call two figures that have the same size and shape?

   congruent   **solid figures**

5. What is another name for a square?

   plane shape   **solid figure**

Measurement Vocabulary

Write the word from the box that belongs in each group.

| day | hour | nickel | ruler | temperature | yard |

1. penny
dime

_____

2. week
month

_____

3. inch
foot

_____

4. quarter hour
half hour

_____

5. thermometer
Celsius

_____

6. measure
length

_____

Write the word that completes the sentence.

7. Chris ate breakfast at 8:00 _____

A.M.   P.M.

8. Jill counted the square tiles that covered her desk to find the desk's

_____.

area   weight

9. Mark drank a _____ of juice for breakfast.

yard   cup

10. The length of a baseball bat is about 1 _____.

centimeter   meter

Getting Ready for the **ISTEP+**

---

1 Which is a way to show eighteen?

○ 8 tens 0 ones

○ 1 ten 8 ones

○ 80

○ 81

---

2 Count by tens.
What are the missing numbers?
Use the hundred chart to help you.

16, 26, 36, _____, _____, _____,

1	2	3	4	5	6	7	8	9	10
11	12	13	14	15	16	17	18	19	20
21	22	23	24	25	26	27	28	29	30
31	32	33	34	35	36	37	38	39	40
41	42	43	44	45	46	47	48	49	50
51	52	53	54	55	56	57	58	59	60
61	62	63	64	65	66	67	68	69	70
71	72	73	74	75	76	77	78	79	80
81	82	83	84	85	86	87	88	89	90
91	92	93	94	95	96	97	98	99	100

37, 38, 39   38, 40, 42   46, 56, 66   56, 66, 76

○   ○   ○   ○

GO ON ▶

3 Compare the numbers.

36   46

○ 36 < 46

○ 36 > 46

○ 36 = 46

○ 46 = 36

GO ON ▶

4 Children voted for their favorite fruit. Use the tally table to fill in the pictograph.

Draw ☺ for every 5 children.

Children's Favorite Fruits	
Fruit	**Tally**
apples	ⅢⅡ ⅢⅡ
bananas	ⅢⅡ
grapes	ⅢⅡ ⅢⅡ ⅢⅡ ⅢⅡ

Children's Favorite Fruits			
apples			
bananas			
grapes			

Key: Each ☺ stands for 5 children.

Use the graph.
How many children chose bananas?

Answer _____ children

Which fruit did the most children choose?

Answer _____

5 Jake has 7 dinosaur stickers. His sister gives him 5 more stickers. Then he buys 3 stickers at the store. How many stickers does Jake have in all?

Show All Work

Answer _____ stickers

Which two numbers did you add first? Why?

_____

_____

6 Jen had 6 bears. Grandma gave her some more. Then Jen had 14 bears. How many bears did Grandma give Jen?

6 + ___ = 14

6   7   8   9
○   ○   ○   ○

GO ON ▶

7 Rosa collects 13 stamps. Amy collects 29 stamps. How many stamps do they collect altogether?

Draw a model to solve.

Draw ▭ for each ten.

Draw ▢ for each one.

Regroup if you need to.

Tens	Ones

Tens	Ones
▢	
1	3
+ 2	9

Answer _____ stamps

8 Add. Find the sum.

Tens	Ones
☐	
2	6
+	4

Tens	Ones

22 ○   28 ○   29 ○   30 ○

9 Add. Find the sum.

Tens	Ones
☐	
2	7
+ 1	8

Tens	Ones

11 ○   35 ○   45 ○   48 ○

GO ON ▶

10 Ari has 42 finger puppets in a box.
He puts 16 puppets on a shelf.
How many puppets are left in the box?

Will you add or subtract to solve? _____

Show All Work

Tens	Ones
☐	☐

Answer _____ puppets

11 Subtract. Find the difference.

Tens	Ones
☐	☐
4	1
−	9

Tens	Ones

32   33   42   50
○   ○   ○   ○

12 Subtract. Find the difference.

Tens	Ones
☐	☐
6	8
− 3	5

Tens	Ones

26   27   33   37
○   ○   ○   ○

GO ON ▶

13 Which addition problem can you use to check this subtraction problem?

$$
\begin{array}{r}
73 \\
- 27 \\
\hline
46
\end{array}
$$

$$
\begin{array}{r}
73 \\
+ 46 \\
\hline
\end{array}
\qquad
\begin{array}{r}
73 \\
+ 27 \\
\hline
\end{array}
\qquad
\begin{array}{r}
27 \\
+ 46 \\
\hline
\end{array}
\qquad
\begin{array}{r}
27 \\
+ 27 \\
\hline
\end{array}
$$

○   ○   ○   ○

---

14 Find the total amount.

_____ ¢,   _____ ¢,   _____ ¢,   _____ ¢,   _____ ¢,

○ 61¢

○ 86¢

○ 95¢

○ 96¢

15 What time does the clock show?

○ 15 minutes past 5

○ half past 5

○ half past 6

○ quarter to 6

16 What time does the clock show?

○ 12:10

○ 12:15

○ 12:20

○ 12:40

GO ON ▶

17 The movie starts at 4:00. It ends at 7:00.
How much time has passed?

Draw hands on the clocks.

Use them as models to solve the problem.

Answer _____ hours

GO ON ▶

18 Use the bar graph.
Which sport did the greatest number of children choose?

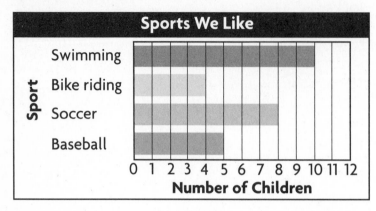

Sports We Like

swimming   bike riding   soccer   baseball

○   ○   ○   ○

19 The shapes in Ty's group have more than 3 sides. Which shape does not belong in Ty's group?

GO ON ▶

20 Which figure has 6 faces, 12 edges, and 8 vertices?

○

○

○

○

21 Which figure is congruent to the figure shown?

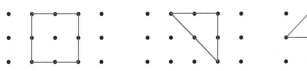

   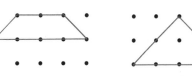   

○   ○   ○   ○

22 Measure to the nearest inch.

- ◯ 3 inches

- ◯ 5 inches

- ◯ 9 inches

- ◯ 13 inches

23 Read the thermometer. What is the temperature?

- ◯ 55° F

- ◯ 60° F

- ◯ 65° F

- ◯ 70° F

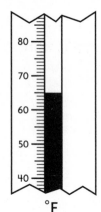

°F

GO ON ▶

Name _____

24 How many cups do two pint containers hold?

      1 pint = 2 cups

○ 2 cups

○ 4 cups

○ 6 cups

○ 8 cups

25 Predict how many tiles will cover the gray shape.

Predict _____ tiles

Draw tiles to test.

Test _____ tiles

Did you predict too many or too few? Explain.

_____

_____

STOP ▮

Getting Ready for the **ISTEP+**

---

1 Use the related fact to complete.

$7 + 5 = 12$, so $12 - 5 = $ ▪

12	7	5	0
Ⓐ	Ⓑ	Ⓒ	Ⓓ

---

2 Members of Sam's bike club rode 17 miles in all. They stopped for a snack when they had 8 miles left to go. How many miles had they gone before stopping for the snack?

Show All Work

Answer _____ miles

Explain how you found your answer.

_____

_____

_____

_____

GO ON ▶

3 Paul bought three packs of party favors. One pack had 6 favors. Another pack had 8 favors. The third pack had 4 favors. How many party favors did Paul buy?

(A) 21 party favors

(B) 20 party favors

(C) 18 party favors

(D) 17 party favors

4 On Saturday, 36 people came to an exhibit. On Sunday, 55 people came. How many people in all came to the exhibit on those two days?

(A) 71 people

(B) 81 people

(C) 91 people

(D) 101 people

GO ON ▶

5 Find the sum.

$$\begin{array}{r} 25 \\ 51 \\ + 14 \\ \hline \end{array}$$

90   81   70   61
Ⓐ   Ⓑ   Ⓒ   Ⓓ

6 Find the difference.

$$\begin{array}{r} 61 \\ - 28 \\ \hline \end{array}$$

109   99   47   33
Ⓐ   Ⓑ   Ⓒ   Ⓓ

7 What is the difference between the speed of the West Indian butterfly and the speed of the hornet?

Ⓐ   43 miles per hour

Ⓑ   17 miles per hour

Ⓒ   9 miles per hour

Ⓓ   7 miles per hour

FASTEST FLYING INSECTS	
Insect	Miles per Hour
Dragonfly	18
Bumblebee	11
West Indian butterfly	30
Hornet	13
Honeybee	7

GO ON ▶

8 Marla's dad drove 18 miles to work. His trip home was 5 miles longer because he stopped at a store. How many miles did he drive from work to home?

Choose the operation. Write a number sentence to solve.

Show All Work

Answer _____ miles

Explain how you decided which operation to use.

_____

_____

_____

GO ON ▶

9 Which number is even?

(A) 233

(B) 336

(C) 243

(D) 629

10 What is the standard form for three hundred nine?

(A) 3,009

(B) 390

(C) 309

(D) 39

GO ON ▶

11 What is the number in standard form?

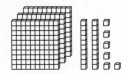

- **A** 326

- **B** 320

- **C** 306

- **D** 56

12 What is the value of the 8 in 285?

- **A** 8 ones

- **B** 8 tens

- **C** 8 hundreds

- **D** 8 thousands

GO ON ▶

13 Which is another way to write five hundred nineteen?

(A) 5 + 1 + 9

(B) 50 + 10 + 9

(C) 500 + 90

(D) 500 + 10 + 9

14 Zack used base-ten blocks to model a number.

What number did Zack model?

Answer _____

Draw base-ten blocks. Show another way to model Zack's number.

Explain how you know your model shows the same number as Zack's model.

_____

_____

_____

GO ON ▶

15 Predict which number comes next in the pattern.

5, 16, 27, 38, _____

(A) 39

(B) 43

(C) 48

(D) 49

16 Which is a correct way to compare the numbers?

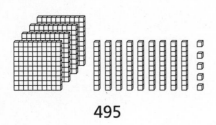   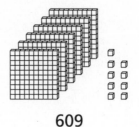

495   609

(A) 495 > 609

(B) 609 < 495

(C) 495 < 609

(D) 495 = 609

17 Which shows the numbers in order from GREATEST to LEAST?

(A) 390; 556; 417

(B) 390; 417; 556

(C) 417; 390; 556

(D) 556; 417; 390

GO ON ▶

18 Use the bar graph. Order the planets by size from LARGEST to SMALLEST.

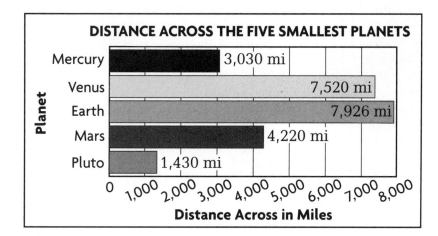

DISTANCE ACROSS THE FIVE SMALLEST PLANETS

Planet	
Mercury	3,030 mi
Venus	7,520 mi
Earth	7,926 mi
Mars	4,220 mi
Pluto	1,430 mi

Distance Across in Miles

Answer _____

_____

_____

_____

_____

Explain how you decided.

_____

_____

_____

GO ON ▶

19 Pam rounded 591 to the nearest ten, and then to the nearest hundred. Which numbers should Pam have rounded to?

(A) 590 and 600

(B) 600 and 600

(C) 590 and 500

(D) 600 and 500

20 Use data from the table. Rounded to the nearest ten, how many mammals does the zoo have?

ZOO ANIMALS	
Type	**Number**
Mammals	214
Birds	428
Reptiles	174

(A) 200

(B) 210

(C) 220

(D) 300

STOP ■

Getting Ready for the **ISTEP**+

---

1 Craig buys a game that costs $4.98 and a book that costs $6.35. Use front-end estimation to estimate the sum.

$4.98
+$6.35

$6.00	$8.00	$10.00	$14.00
Ⓐ	Ⓑ	Ⓒ	Ⓓ

---

2 Find the sum.

372
+249

621	571	521	511
Ⓐ	Ⓑ	Ⓒ	Ⓓ

---

3 Find the sum.

2,625
+ 498

4,123	3,123	3,113	2,023
Ⓐ	Ⓑ	Ⓒ	Ⓓ

GO ON ▶

4 Jane saved $55.75 in October. She saved $24.95 in November. How much money did she save in the two months?

Solve the problem. Then estimate to check.

Show All Work

Answer $ _____

Use the lines below. Explain how you know your answer is reasonable.

_____

_____

_____

_____

_____

_____

GO ON ▶

5 Jim had 43 coins. At a coin show he got 22 more. How many coins did he have in all?

(A) 45 coins

(B) 53 coins

(C) 63 coins

(D) 65 coins

6 What is the missing number?

$315 - \blacksquare = 287$

(A) 14

(B) 28

(C) 34

(D) 36

GO ON ▶

7 Which number sentence is missing a plus sign (+)?

(A) 20 ● 3 = 17

(B) 54 ● 26 = 28

(C) 215 ● 110 = 105

(D) 562 ● 314 = 876

8 One year 2,930 people attended the air show. The next year 6,375 people came. ABOUT how many more people came the second year?

(A) about 9,000 more people

(B) about 3,000 more people

(C) about 2,000 more people

(D) about 400 more people

GO ON ▶

9 Use the model. Find the difference.

437
−128

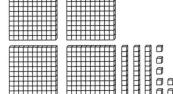

311
Ⓐ

309
Ⓑ

301
Ⓒ

211
Ⓓ

10 Find the difference.

500
−368

132
Ⓐ

138
Ⓑ

142
Ⓒ

242
Ⓓ

11 Wendi picked 187 apricots. She used 166 apricots to make jam. How many apricots did Wendi have left?

Ⓐ 11 apricots

Ⓑ 15 apricots

Ⓒ 21 apricots

Ⓓ 27 apricots

GO ON ▶

Decide whether you need an exact answer or an estimate. Then solve.

Karla is at the pet store. She has $25.00 to spend. She wants to buy a birdcage that costs $18.75, a bird swing that costs $5.59, and birdseed that costs $4.25. Does Karla have enough money?

Show All Work

Answer _____

Explain how you decided whether you needed an exact answer or an estimate.

_____

_____

_____

_____

GO ON ▶

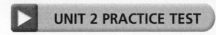
13 Find the amount.

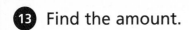

$2.32 $2.17 $2.12 $1.62
Ⓐ   Ⓑ   Ⓒ   Ⓓ

14 Find the amount.

$3.25 $3.40 $3.65 $3.80
Ⓐ   Ⓑ   Ⓒ   Ⓓ

GO ON ▶

15 Count each amount and compare.
Who has more money?

Darla's money

Ken's money

(A) Darla, because $4.37 > $4.52.

(B) Ken, because $4.52 > $4.37.

(C) Ken, because $4.52 < $4.37.

(D) Each has the same amount of money.

GO ON ▶

16 Pat has $4.00. Does she have enough money to buy a pen that costs $1.50 and a birthday card that costs $2.95?

Draw or use play money to solve.

Show All Work

Answer _____

On the lines below, explain how you know.

_____

_____

_____

_____

_____

GO ON ▶

17 Which clock shows two twenty-six?

Ⓐ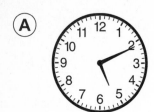

Ⓑ

Ⓒ

Ⓓ

GO ON ▷

18 Use the clocks to find the elapsed time.

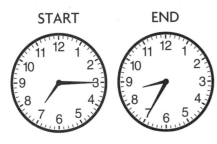

START   END

7:15 A.M.   8:35 A.M.

(A) 20 minutes

(B) 1 hour 5 minutes

(C) 1 hour 20 minutes

(D) 1 hour 30 minutes

19 Find the missing number.

3 weeks = ■ days

(A) 30

(B) 28

(C) 21

(D) 14

GO ON ▶

20 The table shows men's World Cup soccer championships. Use the table. Add a point to the time line for each year. Label each point with the name of the country and the year.

WORLD CUP SOCCER	
Men's Championship	
Country	Year
Brazil	2002
Argentina	1978
West Germany	1990
Brazil	1994
Argentina	1996

1970   1980   1990   2000   2010

France won the World Cup in soccer in 1998. Between which two countries should it be placed on the time line?

Answer _____

Italy won the World Cup in soccer in 1982. Between which two countries should it be placed on the time line?

Answer _____

STOP ■

Getting Ready for the **ISTEP+**

---

1 Lance puts 6 decals on each of his model planes. He has 3 model planes.

Which number sentence can you use to find out how many decals Lance uses?

(A) $6 + 3 = \blacksquare$

(B) $6 + 6 + 6 = \blacksquare$

(C) $3 + 3 + 3 = \blacksquare$

(D) $6 + 6 = \blacksquare$

---

2 What is the product?

$$\blacksquare = 5 \times 5$$

25   35   50   55
(A)   (B)   (C)   (D)

GO ON ▶

3 Use the Order Property of Multiplication.
Which multiplication sentences match the arrays?

(A) 5 x 5 = 25 and 5 x 5 = 25

(B) 3 x 6 = 18 and 6 x 3 = 18

(C) 3 x 5 = 15 and 5 x 3 = 15

(D) 2 x 5 = 10 and 5 x 2 = 10

4 Use the number line to find the product.

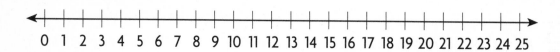

0 1 2 3 4 5 6 7 8 9 10 11 12 13 14 15 16 17 18 19 20 21 22 23 24 25

$3 \times 7 =$ ▪

10	21	22	29
(A)	(B)	(C)	(D)

GO ON ▶

5 Solve if there is too much information. Tell what is missing if there is too little information.

Eight friends played miniature golf. Tickets cost $5 for each person. Next the friends rode bicycles for 45 minutes. Then they shared 3 large pizzas. How much did it cost for the 8 friends to play miniature golf?

Solve. **Show All Work**	or	Tell what is missing.
		_____
		_____
		_____
		_____
		_____
		_____
		_____
		_____
Answer $_____		

GO ON ▶

6 Tyson starts a number pattern. He says
0, 3, 6, 9. What are the next three numbers
in Tyson's pattern?

Use the number line to find Tyson's pattern
rule. Then find the next three numbers.

Rule _____

Next Three Numbers _____

7 Use the Order Property of Multiplication.
Find the product.

$4 \times 8 = 8 \times 4 = $ ▓

24	28	30	32
Ⓐ	Ⓑ	Ⓒ	Ⓓ

GO ON ▶

8 Find the product.

$$\blacksquare = 7 \times 5$$

25　　　　　　35　　　　　　45　　　　　　75

Ⓐ　　　　　　Ⓑ　　　　　　Ⓒ　　　　　　Ⓓ

9 Which number completes the table?

×	5	6	7	8	9
4	20	24	28	■	36

35　　　　　　34　　　　　　32　　　　　　12

Ⓐ　　　　　　Ⓑ　　　　　　Ⓒ　　　　　　Ⓓ

10 Find the missing factor.

$$9 \times \blacksquare = 30 - 3$$

7　　　　　　6　　　　　　4　　　　　　3

Ⓐ　　　　　　Ⓑ　　　　　　Ⓒ　　　　　　Ⓓ

GO ON ▷

11 Multiply. If you wish, break down the array into smaller arrays to help you find the product.

$$7 \times 6 = \blacksquare$$

(A) 13

(B) 36

(C) 40

(D) 42

GO ON ▶

12 It was Sandi's turn to bring snacks to team practice. She brought 4 boxes of granola bars. Each box had 8 bars. How many granola bars did Sandi bring in all?

Use the smaller arrays to help you solve the problem.

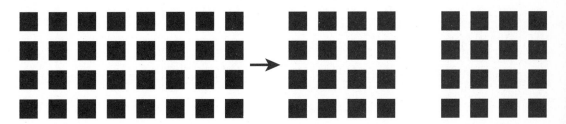

(A) 16 granola bars

(B) 24 granola bars

(C) 32 granola bars

(D) 48 granola bars

GO ON ▶

13 Sarah took a survey about students' favorite beach activities. Each student got one vote. Use the graph to answer the questions.

FAVORITE BEACH ACTIVITIES

Wading	☺ ☺ ☺ ☺ ☺
Swimming	☺ ☺ ☺ ☺ ☺ ☺ ☺
Making sand castles	☺ ☺ ☺
Collecting seashells	☺ ☺ ☺ ☺ ☺ ☾

Key: Each ☺ = 4 students.

How many more students voted for swimming than for wading?

Show All Work

Answer _____ more students

How many more students voted for swimming than for making sand castles?

Show All Work

Answer _____ more students

On the lines below, explain how you found your answers.

_____

_____

_____

_____

GO ON ▶

14 Ben made these tables. To find an 8's fact, he finds a 4's fact and doubles the product. What product should he write to complete the table?

×	1	2	3	4	5	6	7
4	4	8	12	16	20	24	28

×	1	2	3	4	5	6	7
8	8	16	24	32	40	48	■

49
Ⓐ

52
Ⓑ

54
Ⓒ

56
Ⓓ

15 Find the product.

$$9 \times 5 = ■$$

Ⓐ 35

Ⓑ 39

Ⓒ 45

Ⓓ 59

GO ON ▶

16 Ten students can sit at each lunch table. How many students can sit at three tables? Use the number line to find the product.

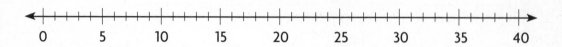

(A) 3 students

(B) 10 students

(C) 15 students

(D) 30 students

17 Find a rule. Which numbers complete the table?

Puzzles	2	3	4	5	6	7	8
Cost	$12	$18	$24	▪	▪	▪	▪

(A) $30, $36, $42, $48

(B) $26, $32, $38, $44

(C) $25, $26, $27, $28

(D) $24, $28, $32, $36

GO ON ▶

18 Find the product.

$$10 \times (2 \times 4) = \blacksquare$$

(A) 18

(B) 40

(C) 60

(D) 80

19 Find the missing number.

$$4 \times 9 = 9 \times \blacksquare$$

(A) 9

(B) 4

(C) 1

(D) 0

GO ON ▶

20 Sam and Kevin played a board game with play money. At the end of the game, Sam had six $5 bills and four $1 bills. Kevin had nine $5 bills and two $1 bills.

The winner was the player with more money at the end. Who won, and by how much?

Show All Work

Answer _____

STOP ■

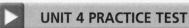
Getting Ready for the **ISTEP+**

---

1 Three brothers share 18 game tokens equally.
How many tokens does each boy get?

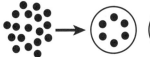

(A) 3 tokens

(B) 4 tokens

(C) 6 tokens

(D) 8 tokens

---

2 Which number sentence does the model show?

$$\begin{array}{cccccc}
24 & 20 & 16 & 12 & 8 & 4 \\
-\ 4 & -\ 4 & -\ 4 & -\ 4 & -\ 4 & -\ 4 \\
\hline
20 & 16 & 12 & 8 & 4 & 0
\end{array}$$

$24 \div 8 = 4$ $24 + 24 = 48$ $24 \times 6 = 144$ $24 \div 4 = 6$

(A)   (B)   (C)   (D)

GO ON ▶

3 Use the number line to solve.

$15 \div 3 = \blacksquare$

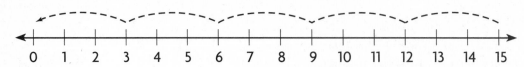

3	5	12	15
Ⓐ	Ⓑ	Ⓒ	Ⓓ

4 Choose +, −, ×, or ÷ to make the number sentence true.

$3 \bullet 7 = 30 - 9$

+	−	×	÷
Ⓐ	Ⓑ	Ⓒ	Ⓓ

5 Which completes the number sentences? Use the array.

$5 \times \blacksquare = 30$ and $30 \div 5 = \blacksquare$

0	1	5	6
Ⓐ	Ⓑ	Ⓒ	Ⓓ

GO ON ▶

6 Find the number that the variable stands for.

$20 \div 4 = a$

$a = \underline{\ ?\ }$

(A) 6

(B) 5

(C) 4

(D) 2

7 Find the other three sentences in the fact family.

$2 \times 8 = 16$

(A) $8 \times 2 = 16,\ 16 \div 2 = 8,\ 16 \div 8 = 2$

(B) $8 \times 1 = 8,\ 8 \div 1 = 8,\ 8 \div 8 = 1$

(C) $4 \times 4 = 16,\ 16 \div 4 = 4,\ 16 - 4 = 12$

(D) $7 \times 2 = 14,\ 14 \div 2 = 7,\ 14 \div 7 = 2$

GO ON ▶

8 There are 24 members in the marching band. They want to march with 6 members in each row. How many rows will there be?

Write a number sentence to solve.

Show All Work

Answer _____ rows

Suppose they decide to march with 4 members in each row. How many rows will there be?

Write a number sentence to solve.

Show All Work

Answer _____ rows

On the lines below, tell how you found your answers.

_____

_____

_____

GO ON ▶

9 Which numbers complete the table?

÷	25	30	35	40	45
5	■	■	■	■	■

(A) 6, 7, 8, 9, 10

(B) 5, 6, 7, 8, 9

(C) 2, 4, 6, 8, 10

(D) 1, 2, 3, 4, 5

10 Which multiplication fact can you use to find the quotient?

$36 \div 4 = $ ■

(A) $6 \times 6 = 36$

(B) $4 \times 7 = 28$

(C) $4 \times 8 = 32$

(D) $4 \times 9 = 36$

GO ON ▷

11 Choose +, −, ×, or ÷ to complete the equation.

$32 \bullet 8 = 12 - 8$

(A) +

(B) −

(C) ×

(D) ÷

12 There were 27 boys and girls at soccer practice. The coach put them into groups of 3 to practice dribbling.

Which number sentence can you use to find out how many groups there were?

(A) $27 \times 3 = \blacksquare$

(B) $27 \div 3 = \blacksquare$

(C) $27 - 3 = \blacksquare$

(D) $27 + 3 = \blacksquare$

GO ON ▶

13 Megan and her mother made 18 candles using sand from the beach, melted wax, and seashells. They put 5 shells around each candle. They put 3 candles in each gift bag. How many gift bags did they fill?

Choose the operation. Then write an equation to solve.

Show All Work

Answer _____ gift bags

On the lines below, tell how you can check your answer.

_____

_____

_____

_____

_____

GO ON ▶

14 Which multiplication fact can you use to find the quotient? What is the quotient?

$48 \div 6 = $ ■

(A) $8 \times 4 = 32$, 4

(B) $7 \times 7 = 49$, 7

(C) $6 \times 7 = 42$, 7

(D) $6 \times 8 = 48$, 8

15 Which numbers complete the table?

÷	24	32	40	48
8	■	■	■	■

(A) 2, 3, 4, 5

(B) 3, 4, 5, 6

(C) 4, 5, 6, 7

(D) 5, 6, 7, 8

GO ON ▶

16 Each plum pie uses 9 plums. Kelly has 90 fresh plums. How many plum pies can she make?

Show how you can use a related multiplication fact to find 90 ÷ 9.

Show All Work

How many plum pies can Kelly make?

Answer _____ plum pies

GO ON ▶

17 Choose +, −, ×, or ÷ to make the number sentence true.

54 ● 9 = 3 × 2

Ⓐ +

Ⓑ −

Ⓒ ×

Ⓓ ÷

18 The model shows how 7 people share 42 apples. Which number sentence shows how many apples each person gets?

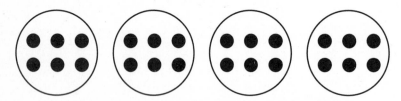

Ⓐ 49 ÷ 7 = 7

Ⓑ 42 ÷ 7 = 6

Ⓒ 6 × 7 = 42

Ⓓ 7 × 6 = 42

GO ON ▷

19 Trina spends $36 for 4 new wheels for her skates. How much does each wheel cost?

Choose the number sentence that solves the problem.

(A) $36 ÷ 4 = $9

(B) $36 ÷ 6 = $6

(C) $36 × 4 = $144

(D) $36 − 4 = $32

GO ON ▶

20 Lana works at an amusement park. She sells visors for $10 each and water bottles for $1 each. On Saturday, Lana collected $46. She sold 6 water bottles. How many visors did she sell?

Work backward to solve.

Show All Work

Answer _____ visors

On Tuesday, Lana put the visors on sale for $5 each. She collected $43 that day. She sold 8 water bottles. How many visors did she sell?

Show All Work

Answer _____ visors

On the lines below, tell how you found the answers.

_____

_____

_____

STOP ■

Name _____

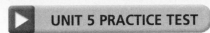

Getting Ready for the **ISTEP+**

---

1 Which field trip was the favorite of the greatest number of students?

FAVORITE FIELD TRIP	
Ice cream factory	15
Airport	13
Fire station	21
Television station	12

(A) ice cream factory

(B) airport

(C) fire station

(D) television station

---

2 Nedim and Max played Sum Roll. They rolled two number cubes 15 times and recorded the sums. Their results were
5, 10, 9, 8, 7, 7, 10, 10, 8, 7, 7, 8, 6, 6, 7.

Make a tally table to organize the data. Then find which sum they rolled most often.

Answer _____

For 3–4, use the line plot and circle graph.

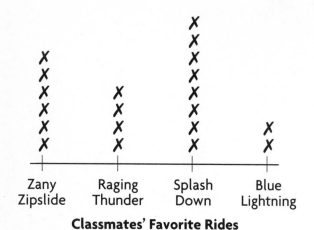

Classmates' Favorite Rides

CLASSMATES' FAVORITE RIDES

3 Whitney took a survey to find her classmates' favorite ride at the amusement park. Which ride was the most popular?

Ⓐ Zany Zipslide

Ⓑ Raging Thunder

Ⓒ Splash Down

Ⓓ Blue Lightning

4 How many votes does the whole circle stand for?

Ⓐ 20 votes   Ⓒ 6 votes

Ⓑ 8 votes   Ⓓ 4 votes

GO ON ▶

5 Emma drew a picture to show how many ears of fresh corn she picked each day. Find the median.

> The **median** is the middle number in an ordered set of data.

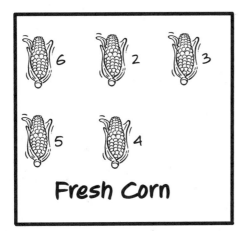

Fresh Corn

6	5	4	3
Ⓐ	Ⓑ	Ⓒ	Ⓓ

6 Which two students have the same mean score?

> The **mean** is the average of an ordered set of data.

Ⓐ Jen and Carl

Ⓑ Carl and Luz

Ⓒ Carl and Suleel

Ⓓ Jen and Suleel

QUIZ SCORES			
Jen	Carl	Luz	Suleel
3	5	3	2
4	2	6	5
4	4	6	3
1	5	5	2

GO ON ▶

7 Use the pictograph to answer the questions.

STUDENTS' PENCILS

Tia	✏✏✏✏✏✏✏
Evan	✏✏✏✏✏✏✏✏✏
Omer	✏✏✏✏✏
Steven	✏✏✏✏✏✏✏✏✏✏✏✏

Each ✏ = 2 pencils

Which student has the greatest number of pencils?

Answer _____

Which student has the least number of pencils?

Answer _____

How many pencils do the two students have together?

Show All Work

Answer _____ pencils

Explain how you used the pictograph to find your answer.

_____

_____

_____

GO ON ▶

8 Use the bar graph to solve.

How many more visitors were there on Saturday than on Friday?

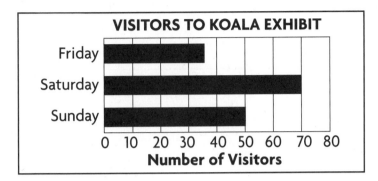

VISITORS TO KOALA EXHIBIT

Friday
Saturday
Sunday

0 10 20 30 40 50 60 70 80
Number of Visitors

A 70 more visitors

C 35 more visitors

B 40 more visitors

D 30 more visitors

9 Use the line graph to solve.

If the trend continues, which might be a reasonable prediction for the next month?

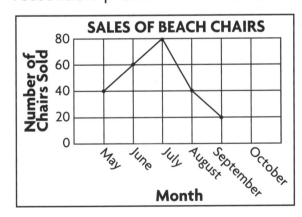

SALES OF BEACH CHAIRS

Number of Chairs Sold

80
60
40
20
0

May June July August September October

Month

A Sales will decrease.

C Sales will increase sharply.

B Sales will increase.

D Sales will stay the same.

GO ON ▶

10 Measure the length of the pencil to the nearest half inch.

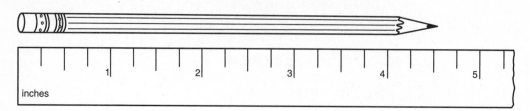

(A) 5 inches

(C) 4 inches

(B) $4\frac{1}{2}$ inches

(D) $3\frac{1}{2}$ inches

11 Measure the length of the eraser to the nearest half inch.

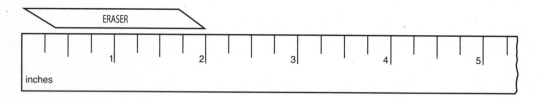

(A) 1 inch

(C) 2 inches

(B) $1\frac{1}{2}$ inches

(D) $2\frac{1}{2}$ inches

GO ON ▶

12 Choose the best unit of measure.

Paul's tent holds three sleeping bags. At the center of the tent, its height is 5 __?__ tall.

(A) inches

(B) feet

(C) yards

(D) miles

13 Choose the best estimate.

Mrs. Liu makes berry smoothies in her blender. ABOUT how much does her blender hold?

(A) about 1 quart

(B) about 1 mile

(C) about 1 yard

(D) about 1 cup

GO ON ▶

14 Choose the best estimate.

Teresa bought a bunch of six bananas. ABOUT how much did six bananas weigh?

(A) about 2 ounces

(B) about 2 gallons

(C) about 2 quarts

(D) about 2 pounds

15 Dan made his toy race car track longer. He added two extra pieces of track. One piece was 12 inches long. The other piece was 14 inches long. How much longer did he make his toy race car track?

(A) 3 feet longer

(B) 2 feet 6 inches longer

(C) 2 feet 2 inches longer

(D) 25 inches longer

GO ON ▶

16 Kathy was washing the car. She ran out of window cleaner for the windshield.

Her dad told her how to make homemade window cleaner to finish the job. He said to add 1 cup of vinegar to a bucket of water.

Should Kathy estimate or measure the amount of water?

Answer _____

Estimate how many quarts of window cleaner one bucket might make.

Answer _____ quarts

Explain why your estimate is reasonable.

_____

_____

_____

_____

GO ON ▶

17 Tate bought two packages of fringe for new curtains.

Each package had 250 centimeters of fringe. How many centimeters is that in all?

Show All Work

Answer _____ centimeters

Complete the table to find how many METERS Tate brought in all.

Centimeters	100				
Meters	1				

Answer Tate bought _____ meters of fringe.

GO ON ▶

18 Hank bought 5 goldfish and a fish tank. Choose the best estimate for the amount of water he needs to fill the tank.

(A) 40 meters

(C) 40 milliliters

(B) 40 centimeters

(D) 40 liters

19 Jim's class got a new computer monitor.

Choose the best estimate for the mass of the monitor.

(A) 15 grams

(C) 15 centimeters

(B) 15 kilograms

(D) 15 liters

GO ON ▶

20 If the outdoor temperature is 80° Fahrenheit, what do you know about the Celsius temperature that day?

(A) It is higher than 80°C.

(B) It is less than 80°C.

(C) It is 80°C.

(D) It is 100°C.

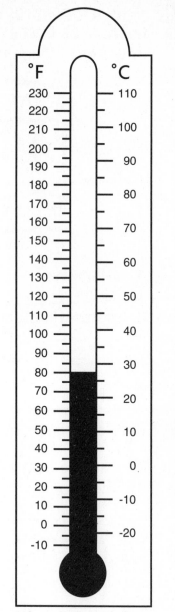

STOP ■

Getting Ready for the ISTEP+

---

1 Which figure is a point?

(A)

(B) •

(C) •——————→

(D) •——————•

---

2 Draw and label one line and one line segment.

On the lines below, tell how they are alike and
how they are different.

_____

_____

_____

3 Describe the figure used for a school zone sign.

Ⓐ quadrilateral, 4 sides and 4 angles

Ⓑ octagon, 8 sides and 8 angles

Ⓒ hexagon, 6 sides and 6 angles

Ⓓ pentagon, 5 sides and 5 angles

4 Which triangle has a right angle?

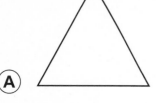 Ⓐ

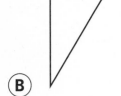 Ⓑ

 Ⓒ

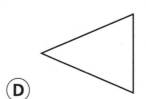 Ⓓ

GO ON ▶

5 Which of these is NOT a quadrilateral?

(A)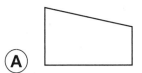

(C)

(B)

(D)

6 Which figure is congruent to the figure below?

(A)

(C)

(B)

(D)

Name _____

7 Which line is a line of symmetry?

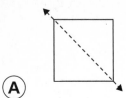 Ⓐ

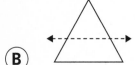 Ⓑ

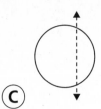 Ⓒ

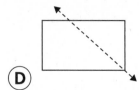 Ⓓ

8 Debra drew how a figure looked with its reflection in a mirror.

Draw all lines of symmetry on the figure that Debra drew.

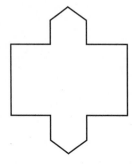

GO ON ▶

9 Use a different combination of pattern blocks to make a parallelogram that is congruent to this one. Draw the figure that you make.

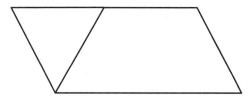

Explain how you know the figures are congruent.

_____

_____

_____

10 Which solid figure has the faces shown?

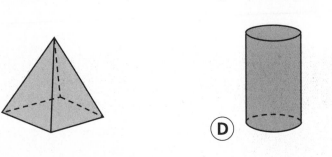

(A)

(C)

(B)

(D)

11 A cube has 6 faces. How many faces do 5 cubes have?

(A) 5 faces

(C) 11 faces

(B) 6 faces

(D) 30 faces

GO ON ▶

12 Name the solid figures used to make the object.

(A) cone, cylinder, rectangular pyramid

(B) cone, cylinder, cube

(C) sphere, cone, cube

(D) sphere, cylinder, cube

13 Which figure is a top view of a sphere?

(A)

(C)

(B)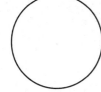

(D)

GO ON ▶

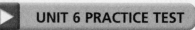

14 Find the perimeter.

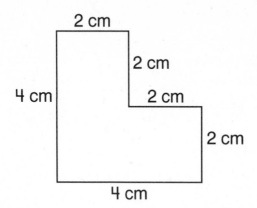

A) 10 cm   C) 16 cm

B) 12 cm   D) 18 cm

15 Find the perimeter.

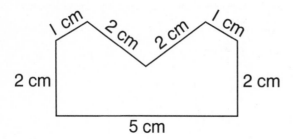

A) 11 cm

B) 13 cm

C) 14 cm

D) 15 cm

GO ON ▶

16 Find the area of the figure in square units.

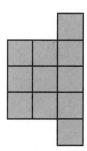

(A)   3 square units

(B)   11 square units

(C)   16 square units

(D)   18 square units

17 Find the area of the figure in square units.

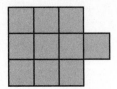

- Ⓐ 12 square units

- Ⓑ 10 square units

- Ⓒ   9 square units

- Ⓓ   3 square units

18 Kendra wants to plant flowers and put a fence around them. She has 25 feet of fencing. If she wants to have the greatest area possible, how long should her garden be? How wide should it be?

Show All Work

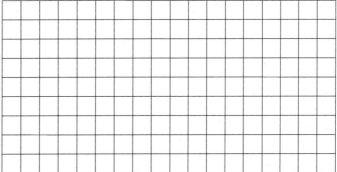

Answer _____

What if she decides to make a smaller garden and use only 16 feet of fencing? If she wants to have the greatest area possible, how long should her garden be? How wide should it be?

Show All Work

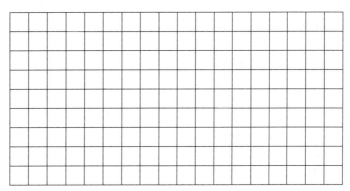

Answer _____

Explain how you used what you know about rectangles and squares to help you solve the problems.

_____

_____

GO ON ▶

19 Find the volume of the solid figure.

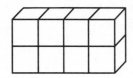

  Ⓐ   8 cubic units

  Ⓑ 12 cubic units

  Ⓒ 14 cubic units

  Ⓓ 22 cubic units

20 Find the volume of the solid figure.

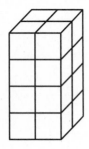

  Ⓐ   8 cubic units

  Ⓑ 12 cubic units

  Ⓒ 16 cubic units

  Ⓓ 24 cubic units

STOP ■

Getting Ready for the **ISTEP+**

1 Name the pattern unit.

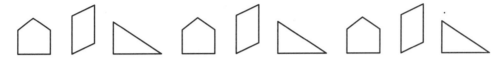

- (A) pentagon, rectangle, triangle

- (B) rhombus, parallelogram

- (C) pentagon, triangle, parallelogram

- (D) pentagon, parallelogram, triangle

2 Tran drew this pattern. What pattern unit did he use?

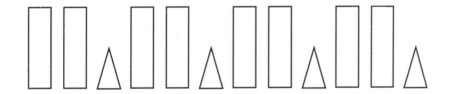

Answer _____

Show the same pattern using the letters A and B.

GO ON ▶

3 What is a rule for the pattern?

●   ● ●   ● ● ● ●   ● ● ● ● ● ● ● ●
●   ● ●   ● ● ● ●   ● ● ● ● ● ● ● ●

Ⓐ Add 2.

Ⓑ Add 4.

Ⓒ Multiply by 2.

Ⓓ Multiply by 4.

4 A rule is multiply by 2. Which numbers come next in the pattern?

5, 10, 20, ____, ____

Ⓐ 25, 30

Ⓑ 30, 40

Ⓒ 40, 60

Ⓓ 40, 80

GO ON ▶

5 Find a rule for the pattern.

105, 117, 129, 141, 153

(A) Add 8.

(B) Add 12.

(C) Add 13.

(D) Multiply by 2.

6 Find a rule. Which numbers are missing?

408, 388, 368, 348, _____, 308, 288, _____

(A) 336, 280

(B) 338, 278

(C) 358, 298

(D) 328, 268

GO ON ▷

7 Which pattern has the rule *multiply by 3*?

(A) 2, 6, 18

(B) 2, 5, 8

(C) 3, 6, 9

(D) 3, 13, 33

8 The managers of the baseball stadium wanted to give free baseballs to ticket holders from each section. They used a pattern to pick the winning tickets. What rule did they use to choose the ticket numbers?

23, 173, 323, 473, 623

(A) Subtract 15.

(B) Subtract 11.

(C) Add 143.

(D) Add 150.

GO ON ▶

9 Rico wrote the following pattern. Which is a rule for Rico's pattern?

105, 98, 91, 84, 77

(A) Subtract 8.

(B) Subtract 7.

(C) Subtract 6.

(D) Add 7.

10 The mail carrier needs to deliver a letter to 654 Bonanza Court. The mail carrier cannot see all of the house numbers. To which house should he deliver the mail for that address?

Find a pattern to solve.

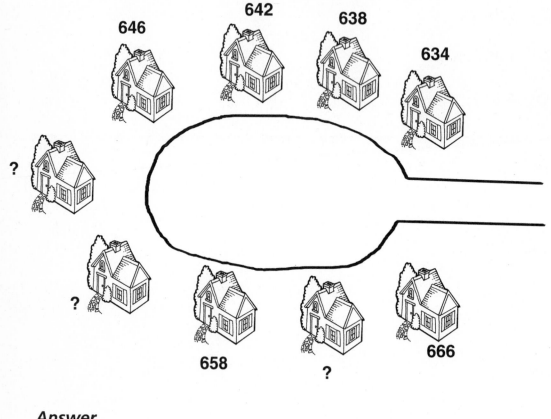

Answer _____

What is a rule for the pattern?

Answer _____

GO ON ▶

11 Is it certain, likely, unlikely, or impossible that spring will follow winter this year?

(**A**) certain

(**B**) likely

(**C**) unlikely

(**D**) impossible

12 Is it certain, likely, unlikely, or impossible for a peach to grow on an apple tree?

(**A**) certain

(**B**) likely

(**C**) unlikely

(**D**) impossible

GO ON ▶

13 What are the possible outcomes of tossing one coin?

(A) tails and tails

(B) heads and heads

(C) heads and tails

(D) heads and tails and tails

14 What are the possible outcomes of using this spinner?

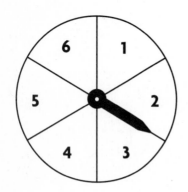

(A) 1, 2, 3, 4, 5, 6

(B) 1, 2, 3

(C) 1, 2, 3, 4, 5

(D) 1

GO ON ▶

15 Draw a spinner in which all of the outcomes are equally likely.

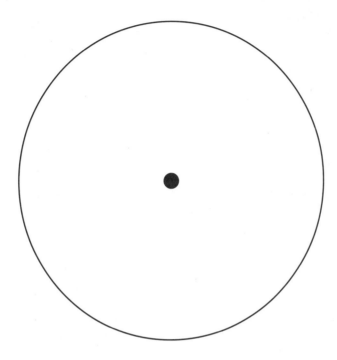

Explain how you know the outcomes are equally likely.

_____

_____

_____

_____

16 Ariel pulls letter tiles from the bag. Which outcome is unlikely?

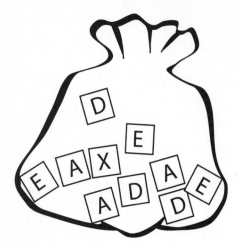

(A) A

(B) D

(C) E

(D) X

17 Amir spins the pointer of this spinner. Which outcomes are equally likely?

(A) 2, 3

(B) 2, 4

(C) 3, 4

(D) 1, 2

GO ON ▶

18 Anisha says she will most likely pull the letter B from the bag. What is her error?

Ⓐ She is most likely to pull the letter C, because there are more Cs than other letters.

Ⓑ She is correct.

Ⓒ She is most likely to pull the letter A, because there are more As than other letters.

Ⓓ She is equally likely to pull an A or a B.

19 The line plot shows the number of smoothies sold at Sam's Smoothies each day for the past two weeks. How many smoothies do you predict Sam will sell tomorrow?

Ⓐ less than 20

Ⓑ less than 30

Ⓒ more than 30

Ⓓ more than 40

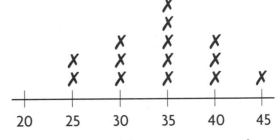

Smoothies Sold in Past Two Weeks

GO ON ▶

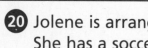

20 Jolene is arranging her trophies on a shelf. She has a soccer trophy, a basketball trophy, and a gymnastics trophy. How many ways can she arrange her trophies?

Show All Work

Answer _____ ways

How did you find the answer? Explain the strategy you used.

_____

_____

_____

STOP ■

Getting Ready for the ISTEP+

---

1 The 4 in the fraction $\frac{3}{4}$ is the _____.

(A) numerator

(B) denominator

(C) addend

(D) sum

---

2 Tom had 5 puzzles. He gave $\frac{2}{5}$ of them to his sister. Which is the numerator in the fraction $\frac{2}{5}$?

(A) 2

(B) 3

(C) 5

(D) 7

GO ON ▶

3 Which fraction is equivalent to $\frac{6}{8}$?

1

$\frac{1}{8}$	$\frac{1}{8}$	$\frac{1}{8}$	$\frac{1}{8}$	$\frac{1}{8}$	$\frac{1}{8}$

A | $\frac{1}{3}$ | $\frac{1}{3}$ |

B | $\frac{1}{3}$ |

C | $\frac{1}{4}$ | $\frac{1}{4}$ |

D | $\frac{1}{4}$ | $\frac{1}{4}$ | $\frac{1}{4}$ |

4 Sal served $\frac{2}{5}$ of a pie. Mel served $\frac{4}{10}$ of a pie the same size. Which statement is true?

Sal's pie

Mel's pie

A Sal served more pie.

B Mel served more pie.

C Sal and Mel served the same amount of pie.

D Sal served less pie.

GO ON ▶

5 Kim has 8 marbles. $\frac{3}{8}$ of the marbles are gray. $\frac{1}{8}$ of the marbles are black. $\frac{4}{8}$ of the marbles are white. Which compares the part that is gray with the part that is black?

Ⓐ $\frac{1}{8} < \frac{4}{8}$

Ⓑ $\frac{3}{8} < \frac{4}{8}$

Ⓒ $\frac{4}{8} > \frac{3}{8}$

Ⓓ $\frac{3}{8} > \frac{1}{8}$

GO ON ▶

6 Draw a model to solve.

Mario is making paste for a piñata. He needs
$\frac{2}{3}$ cup of flour, $\frac{1}{8}$ cup of salt, and $\frac{1}{4}$ cup of water.
Write the ingredients in order from the
greatest to the least.

Show All Work

Answer _____

Of which ingredient does Mario need the least? Explain.

Answer _____

GO ON ▶

7 Find the sum.

| $\frac{1}{9}$ | $\frac{1}{9}$ | $\frac{1}{9}$ |

| $\frac{1}{9}$ | $\frac{1}{9}$ |

$$\frac{3}{9} + \frac{2}{9} = \blacksquare$$

A $\frac{5}{9}$

B $\frac{5}{18}$

C $\frac{3}{18}$

D $\frac{2}{18}$

8 Which is the sum in simplest form?

| $\frac{1}{10}$ | $\frac{1}{10}$ | $\frac{1}{10}$ |

| $\frac{1}{10}$ | $\frac{1}{10}$ |

$$\frac{3}{10} + \frac{2}{10} = \blacksquare$$

A $\frac{5}{20}$

B $\frac{5}{10}$

C $\frac{1}{2}$

D $\frac{2}{2}$

GO ON ▶

9 Juan has a new book to read. He read $\frac{3}{4}$ of the book before supper. How much of his book does Juan have left to read?

1		

$\frac{1}{4}$	$\frac{1}{4}$	$\frac{1}{4}$

$$1 - \frac{3}{4} = \blacksquare$$

(A) $\frac{1}{4}$ of the book

(B) $\frac{5}{8}$ of the book

(C) $\frac{4}{4}$ of the book

(D) $\frac{5}{4}$ of the book

10 Ben had 12 eggs. He used 3 of them to make an omelette. What fraction of the 12 eggs does Ben have left? Find the answer in simplest form.

(A) $\frac{1}{6}$

(B) $\frac{3}{12}$

(C) $\frac{6}{12}$

(D) $\frac{3}{4}$

GO ON ▶

11 Carl and Ana shared a pizza. Carl ate $\frac{3}{8}$ of the pizza and Ana ate $\frac{2}{8}$. Is it reasonable to say that more than $\frac{1}{2}$ of the pizza is left? Explain.

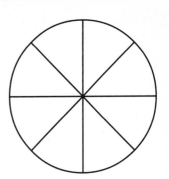

Show All Work

Answer _____

_____

_____

_____

12 Which decimal does the shaded part of the model show?

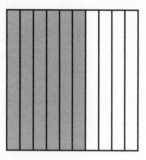

(A) 0.1

(B) 0.4

(C) 0.6

(D) 0.8

13 Which is a fraction for the decimal?

ONES	.	TENTHS
0	.	4

(A) $\frac{40}{10}$

(B) $\frac{10}{40}$

(C) $\frac{1}{4}$

(D) $\frac{4}{10}$

GO ON ▶

14 Which decimal does the shaded part of the model show?

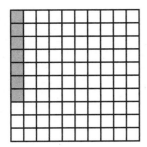

- (A) 0.03
- (B) 0.07
- (C) 0.37
- (D) 0.70

15 Which is NOT another way to write the decimal 3.25?

- (A) 300 + 20 + 5
- (B) three and twenty-five hundredths
- (C) 3 + 0.2 + 0.05
- (D) 3 ones, 2 tenths, 5 hundredths

GO ON ▶

16 Mara biked 2.5 miles to the grocery store. She bought 5 pounds of sugar, 7 pounds of apples, and 1 pound of flour. How heavy were the groceries?

Draw a line under the information you need to solve the problem. Then solve it.

Show All Work

Answer _____ **pounds**

What information in the problem is not needed? Explain how you decided.

_____

_____

_____

_____

GO ON ▶

17 Which does NOT tell the value of a quarter?

(A) $0.25

(B) $0.50

(C) $\frac{1}{4}$ of a dollar

(D) 25 cents

18 Think of dimes as tenths and pennies as hundredths. Which numbers complete the table?

$0.35			
Dollars	.	Dimes	Pennies
0	.	■	■

0, 5
(A)

3, 0
(B)

3, 5
(C)

5, 3
(D)

19 Gerald said that the sum of 0.5 and 0.03 is 0.8. Is he correct? Why or why not?

(A) Yes, because 5 and 3 is 8.

(B) Yes, because 5 tenths and 3 tenths is 8 tenths.

(C) No, because 5 and 3 tenths is 5.3.

(D) No, because 5 tenths and 3 hundredths is 0.53.

GO ON ▶

20 Sharla bought 2 pears and 1 banana. She gave the clerk $5.00. How much change should she get?

Today's Specials	
bananas	$0.15 each
pears	$0.23 each

Show All Work

Answer $ _____

The clerk had dollar bills, dimes, and pennies. What bills and coins might the clerk have given Sharla?

_____

_____

STOP ■

Getting Ready for the ISTEP+

---

1 Use a pattern. Find the product.

$3 \times 4 = 12$

$3 \times 40 = 120$

$3 \times 400 = $ ■

12	120	1,200	12,000
Ⓐ	Ⓑ	Ⓒ	Ⓓ

---

2 Use a pattern. Find the product.

$2 \times 300 = $ ■

6	60	600	6,000
Ⓐ	Ⓑ	Ⓒ	Ⓓ

---

3 Phil is making a pattern.
What number sentence comes next?

$4 \times 5 = 20$
$4 \times 50 = 200$
$4 \times 500 = 2,000$
     ?
   ――――――

Ⓐ $4 \times 500 = 2,000$ Ⓒ $4 \times 2,000 = 8,000$

Ⓑ $4 \times 1,000 = 4,000$ Ⓓ $4 \times 5,000 = 20,000$

GO ON ▶

4 The art teacher has 3 sets of crayons. Each set has 24 crayons. How many crayons are there in all?

Draw base-ten blocks to model the problem. Solve. Write your answer on the line below.

Answer _____ crayons

On the lines below, tell how you found your answer.

_____

_____

_____

_____

GO ON ▶

5 Use the arrays. Find the product.

$3 \times 15 =$ _?_

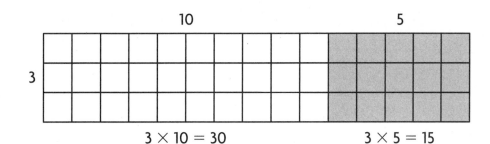

10   5

3

$3 \times 10 = 30$ $3 \times 5 = 15$

25   35   40   45
(A)   (B)   (C)   (D)

6 Paul has 4 photo albums. There are 16 photos in each album. Which shows how Paul can use the arrays to find how many photos he has in all 4 albums?

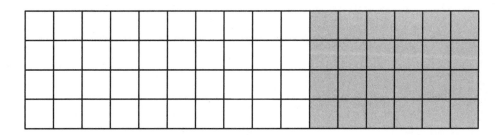

(A) $10 + 4 = 14$ and $6 + 4 = 10$

(B) $4 + 4 + 4 + 4 = 16$

(C) $4 \times 10 = 40$ and $6 + 4 = 10$

(D) $4 \times 10 = 40$ and $4 \times 6 = 24$

GO ON ▶

7 Pam has 4 horses. She buys 20 pounds of feed for each horse. Which shows one way to find how many pounds of feed she buys in all?

(A) Add. $20 + 4 = \blacksquare$

(B) Subtract. $20 - 4 = \blacksquare$

(C) Multiply. $4 \times 20 = \blacksquare$

(D) Divide. $20 \div 4 = \blacksquare$

8 Tyrone made a table of Animal Contest Entries.

Choose the number sentence that shows how to find out how many more rabbits entered than turtles.

ANIMAL CONTEST ENTRIES	
Animal	**Number of Entries**
Rabbits	64
Turtles	40
Birds	32
Fish	25

(A) $64 - 40 = \blacksquare$

(B) $64 + 40 = \blacksquare$

(C) $64 \times 40 = \blacksquare$

(D) $64 \div 40 = \blacksquare$

GO ON ▶

9 Mark has 48 pages left to read and 6 days left to finish reading a book. He wants to read the same number of pages each day. How many pages should he read each day?

Write a number sentence to solve.

Show All Work

Answer _____ pages

On the lines below, explain why you chose that operation.

_____

_____

_____

GO ON ▶

10 Albert bought 2 puzzles for $3.79 each. Then he bought a crossword puzzle book for $4.19. How much did Albert spend?

(A) $3.39

(B) $7.98

(C) $11.77

(D) $15.96

11 Draw a picture to solve.

Marla has 26 pennies. She gives an equal number to each of her cousins—Ben, Pat, and Kimmy. How many pennies does each cousin get? How many pennies are left over?

Show All Work

Answer _____

_____

GO ON ▶

12 Use the model. What is the quotient and remainder?

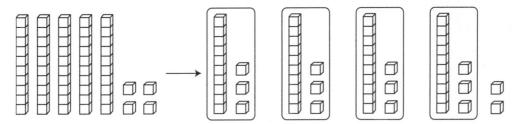

$$54 \div 4$$

(A) 4 r2

(B) 13

(C) 13 r2

(D) 15

13 Choose the division equation that matches the model.

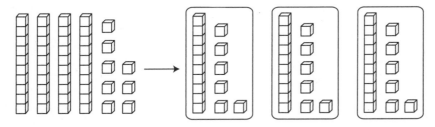

(A) $48 \div 8 = 6$

(B) $48 \div 6 = 8$

(C) $48 \div 4 = 12$

(D) $48 \div 3 = 16$

GO ON ▶

14 Amy has 52¢ to spend on party favors for 4 friends. If she spends the same amount for each friend, what is the most she can spend for each?

Solve the problem. Use an inverse operation to check your answer.

Show All Work

Answer _____ ¢

Explain how you know your answer is correct.

_____

_____

_____

GO ON ▶

15 There are 32 people who want to tour a nature preserve. Only 9 people can go at one time. How many tours should the guide plan so that everyone can take the tour? You can solve the problem using division.

$$32 \div 9 = 3 \text{ r}5$$

Which is the most reasonable solution?

(A) 3 tours

(B) 4 tours

(C) 5 tours

(D) 6 tours

16 Ms. Carlos makes 64 ounces of lemonade. One serving is 6 ounces. Choose the number sentence that shows how many 6-ounce servings Ms. Carlos makes.

(A) $64 - 64 = 0$

(B) $64 \times 6 = 384$

(C) $64 \div 6 = 10 \text{ r}4$

(D) $64 + 6 = 70$

GO ON ▶

17 Ms. Chin gives 5 piano lessons in 120 minutes. Each lesson lasts the same amount of time. How many minutes does each lesson last?

(A) 20 minutes

(B) 24 minutes

(C) 125 minutes

(D) 600 minutes

18 Which number divided by 6 gives a quotient of 21?

(A) 126

(B) 127

(C) 136

(D) 621

GO ON ▶

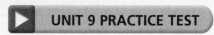
19 Laura is packing peaches. She puts 6 peaches into each basket. She has 228 peaches. How many baskets can she fill?

(A) 38 baskets

(B) 30 baskets

(C) 24 baskets

(D) 12 baskets

20 Mr. Li has 372 pencils to share among 9 classrooms. ABOUT how many pencils can he put in each classroom?

(A) about 10 pencils

(B) about 20 pencils

(C) about 40 pencils

(D) about 80 pencils

STOP

VOCABULARY REVIEW

Number Sense Vocabulary

Write the word or words from the box that best complete the sentence.

compare	decimal	denominator	expanded form	impossible
numerator	outcome	probability	round	tenths

1. The 1 in the fraction $\frac{1}{3}$ is the _____.

2. To decide which of two numbers is greater, you _____ them.

3. You can _____ numbers to help you estimate.

4. The number 0.4 is called a _____.

5. The 3 in the fraction $\frac{2}{3}$ is the _____.

6. The chance that an event will happen is called _____.

7. 300 + 40 + 6 shows the number 346 in _____.

8. An event is _____ if it can never happen.

9. You read the decimal 0.7 as seven _____.

10. The possible result in an experiment is called the _____.

Computation Vocabulary

Circle the correct answer.

1. In which number sentence is 3 a **factor**?

   $2 + 3 = 12$ $3 \times 8 = 32$

   $12 - 9 = 3$ $12 \div 3 = 4$

2. In which number sentence is 5 an **addend**?

   $20 \div 5 = 4$ $5 \times 0 = 0$

   $12 + 5 = 17$ $20 - 5 = 15$

3. In which number sentence is 2 the **quotient**?

   $8 \div 4 = 2$ $2 + 8 = 10$

   $12 \div 2 = 6$ $4 \times 2 = 8$

4. In which number sentence is 3 the **divisor**?

   $27 \div 3 = 9$ $3 + 9 = 12$

   $27 - 3 = 24$ $3 \times 9 = 27$

5. Which pair of number sentences shows
   inverse operations?

   $15 + 5 = 20$ $13 - 8 = 5$ $3 \times 4 = 12$
   $20 - 15 = 5$ $13 - 5 = 8$ $3 + 4 = 7$

Name _____

More Computation Vocabulary

Circle the correct answer.

1. Which four number sentences do NOT make a **fact family**?

$6 + 7 = 13$	$6 \times 2 = 12$	$5 \times 3 = 15$
$7 + 6 = 13$	$6 \times 3 = 18$	$3 \times 5 = 15$
$13 - 6 = 7$	$6 \times 4 = 24$	$15 \div 3 = 5$
$13 - 7 = 6$	$6 \times 5 = 30$	$15 \div 5 = 3$

2. In which problem do you need to **regroup**?

   $$\begin{array}{r} 347 \\ + 512 \\ \hline \end{array} \qquad \begin{array}{r} 239 \\ + 740 \\ \hline \end{array}$$

   $$\begin{array}{r} 382 \\ + 519 \\ \hline \end{array} \qquad \begin{array}{r} 865 \\ + 134 \\ \hline \end{array}$$

3. Which number is most likely to be an **estimate**?

   2.45   341

   $4\frac{1}{2}$ 200

4. Which is an example of the **Commutative Property of Multiplication**?

   $7 \times 5 = 5 \times 7$ $7 \times 0 = 0$

   $(6 + 7) + 3 = 6 + (7 + 3)$ $7 \times 1 = 7$

5. Which group of fractions are **like fractions**?

   $\dfrac{1}{4}, \dfrac{3}{4}, \dfrac{2}{4}$ $\dfrac{2}{4}, \dfrac{4}{8}, \dfrac{1}{7}$ $\dfrac{1}{2}, \dfrac{1}{3}, \dfrac{1}{4}$

Algebra and Functions Vocabulary

Write the word or words that complete the sentence.

1. Another name for a number sentence is a(n) _____.

   equation   factor

2. $12 - 4$ is _____ to 9.

   equal   not equal

3. A part of a number sentence that does not have an equal sign, such as

   3×4, is called an _____.

   addend   expression

4. A(n) _____ shows objects in rows and columns.

   array   fraction

5. The numbers 3, 6, 9, and 12 are all _____ of 3.

   factors   multiples

Draw a line from the multiplication property to the equation it matches.

6. Commutative
   Property   •   • $8 \times 0 = 0$

7. Identity
   Property   •   • $1 \times 3 = 3$

8. Distributive
   Property   •   • $(2 \times 4) \times 3 = 2 \times (4 \times 3)$

9. Zero
   Property   •   • $4 \times 6 = 6 \times 4$

10. Associative
    Property   •   • $6 \times 7 = (6 \times 3) + (6 \times 4)$

Geometry Vocabulary

Circle the correct answer to each clue.

1. I form a square corner and measure 90 degrees.

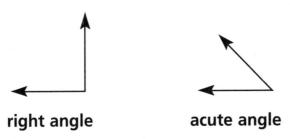

right angle   **acute angle**

2. I have two endpoints and am part of a line.

ray   **line segment**

3. I am a quadrilateral.

square   **triangle**

4. I divide a figure into two equal parts.

line of symmetry   **parallel lines**

5. I have 4 faces that are triangles and one face that is a square.

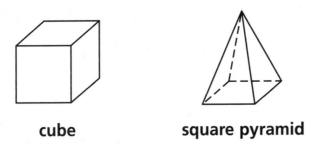

cube   **square pyramid**

Name _____

Measurement Vocabulary

Write the word from the box that completes each group.

| capacity | elapsed time | Fahrenheit | kilogram | meter | weight |

1. mass   gram   _____

2. Celsius   degrees   _____

3. centimeter   kilometer   _____

4. ounce   pound   _____

5. liter   milliliter   _____

Write the word that completes the sentence.

6. There are 120 minutes in 2 _____.
                                 hours   **days**

7. The distance around a figure is called its _____.
                                   perimeter   **area**

8. Groups of coins that have the same value are _____.
                                   variables   **equivalent**

9. Area is measured in _____ units.
                     cubic   **square**

10. _____ is the amount of space a solid figure takes up.
   Volume   **Symmetry**

Getting Ready for the **ISTEP+**

---

1 Choose the operation.
Write a number sentence.
Then solve.

Jane and her family drove 91 miles from Fort
Wayne to Richmond. Then they drove 65 miles
from Richmond to Indianapolis. How many
miles did they drive in all?

Show All Work

Answer _____ miles

---

2 Find the number in standard form.

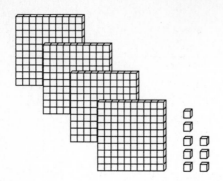

(A) 840

(B) 480

(C) 408

(D) 48

GO ON ▶

3 Which shows the numbers in order from GREATEST to LEAST?

(A) 3,009; 3,173; 3,325

(B) 3,325; 3,009; 3,173

(C) 3,325; 3,173; 3,009

(D) 3,009; 3,325; 3,173

4 Sara buys a book that costs $2.59 and a puzzle that costs $9.45. Round to the nearest dollar to estimate the sum.

$$\begin{array}{r} \$2.59 \\ +\$9.45 \\ \hline \end{array}$$

(A) about $20.00

(B) about $17.00

(C) about $15.00

(D) about $12.00

GO ON ▶

5 Ayana's family drove 112 miles one day from Evansville to Terre Haute. The next day they drove to South Bend, a distance of 218 miles. How many more miles did they drive the second day than the first day?

(A) 106 miles

(B) 130 miles

(C) 196 miles

(D) 330 miles

6 The diameter of Earth is about 7,926 miles. The diameter of Mars is about 4,220 miles. ABOUT how much greater is the diameter of Earth than the diameter of Mars?

Decide whether you need an exact answer or an estimate. Then solve.

(A) exact, 3,606 miles

(B) exact, 3,706 miles

(C) estimate, about 4,000 miles

(D) estimate, about 6,000 miles

GO ON ▶

7 Peter has $10.00. Does he have enough money to buy a game that costs $4.50 and a birthday card that costs $3.95?

Show All Work

Answer _____

Explain how you know.

_____

_____

_____

GO ON ▶

8 Fran went to a movie. The movie started at 5:10. It ended at 6:45. How long did the movie last?

5:10   6:45

(A) 1 hour 35 minutes

(B) 1 hour 30 minutes

(C) 46 minutes

(D) 11 minutes

9 Mia has 3 baskets. She has 8 apples in each basket. How many apples does she have?

Which number sentence can you use to solve the problem?

(A) 8 + 3 = ■

(B) 8 + 8 + 8 = ■

(C) 3 + 3 + 3 = ■

(D) 8 + 8 = ■

GO ON ▶

10 Use the number line to find the product.

$$7 \times 3 = \blacksquare$$

(A) 10

(B) 14

(C) 21

(D) 24

GO ON ▶

11 Find the product.

$$8 \times 5 = \blacksquare$$

Ⓐ 25

Ⓑ 28

Ⓒ 30

Ⓓ 40

12 There are 9 players on a team. How many players are on 8 teams?

Find a rule. Use the table to solve.

Teams	1	2	3	4	5	6	7	8
Players	9	18	27	36	45	54	63	■

Ⓐ 52 players

Ⓑ 60 players

Ⓒ 72 players

Ⓓ 40 players

GO ON ▶

13 Which number completes the number sentence?

$$(8 \times 2) \times 5 = \blacksquare \times (2 \times 5)$$

(A) 2

(B) 5

(C) 8

(D) 16

14 Mrs. Chin bought 2 boxes of pasta. Each box had 14 lasagna noodles. She made 3 pans of lasagna, using 8 noodles for each pan. How many lasagna noodles did she have left over?

Show All Work

Answer _____ lasagna noodles

On the lines below, explain how you solved the problem.

_____

_____

_____

_____

_____

GO ON ▶

15 Find the other three number sentences in the fact family.

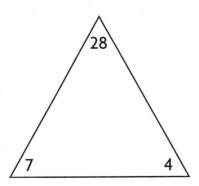

$7 \times 4 = 28$

(A) $7 \times 5 = 35, 35 \div 7 = 5, 35 \div 5 = 7$

(B) $4 \times 6 = 24, 24 \div 4 = 6, 24 \div 6 = 4$

(C) $4 + 7 = 11, 7 - 4 = 3, 7 - 3 = 4$

(D) $4 \times 7 = 28, 28 \div 4 = 7, 28 \div 7 = 4$

GO ON ▶

16 Brandon has 30 cards. He wants to divide the cards equally among 5 friends. How many cards will each friend get?

Write a number sentence to solve.

Show All Work

Answer _____ cards

What if Brandon decides to divide the cards equally among 6 friends? How many cards will each friend get then?

Write a number sentence to solve.

Show All Work

Answer _____ cards

On the lines below, explain how you solved the problems.

_____

_____

_____

_____

GO ON ▶

17 Choose +, −, ×, or ÷ to complete the equation.

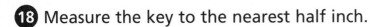

56 ● 7 = 4 × 2

+   −   ×   ÷
A   **B**   **C**   **D**

18 Measure the key to the nearest half inch.

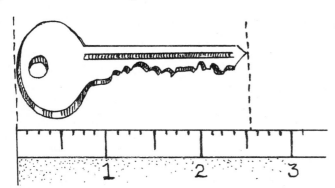

A 1 inch   **C** 2 inches

B $1\frac{1}{2}$ inches   **D** $2\frac{1}{2}$ inches

19 Which figure shows a line of symmetry?

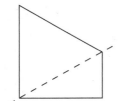
A

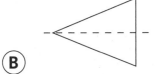
B

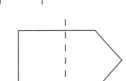
C

D

20 Find the perimeter.

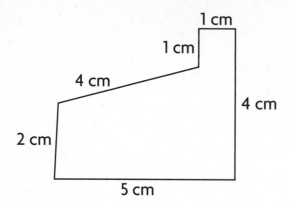

1 cm

1 cm

4 cm

4 cm

2 cm

5 cm

(A) 17 cm

(B) 15 cm

(C) 13 cm

(D) 11 cm

21 Look at the pattern. Which rule describes this pattern?

   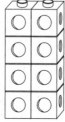

(A) Add 2.

(C) Multiply by 2.

(B) Add 4.

(D) Multiply by 4.

GO ON ▶

22 The 2 in the fraction $\frac{1}{2}$ is the ____.

(A) numerator

(B) denominator

(C) addend

(D) sum

23 Mrs. Salcedo used chalk to divide her driveway into 6 equal sections. Ana decorated $\frac{2}{6}$ of the sections. Pablo also decorated $\frac{2}{6}$ of the sections. Is it reasonable to say that Ana and Pablo decorated more than $\frac{1}{2}$ of the driveway? Why?

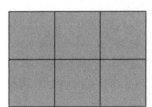

(A) No, because $\frac{2}{6} = \frac{2}{6}$

(B) No, because $\frac{1}{2} > \frac{2}{6}$

(C) Yes, because $\frac{1}{6} < \frac{2}{6}$

(D) Yes, because $\frac{4}{6} > \frac{1}{2}$

GO ON ▶

24 Which decimal does the shaded part of the model show?

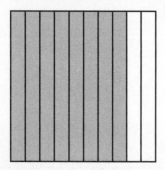

0.5
Ⓐ

0.7
Ⓑ

0.8
Ⓒ

0.10
Ⓓ

25 Five students have to share one box of 26 pencils. Can they share 26 pencils equally?

Draw a picture to solve. Explain your answer.

Answer _____

_____

_____

STOP ▮